Introduction

This tome of tantalising teasers has its roots in an unbridled passion for collecting snippets on my Norfolk rounds as writer, broadcaster and nosy native. I'm still loitering and learning.

My fervent hope in asking so many questions about this matchless part of the world is to whet appetites to find out more. Here are signposts to hundreds of discovery trails. Newcomers and visitors should treat the following pages as a useful primer while locals ought to be magnanimous enough to turn them as a refresher. All ought to find a genuine measure of entertainment.

I recall teasing the young Skipper lads with loads of information about people and places on our family outings before they fell asleep in the back of the car. A trip round the Burnhams brought the inevitable: "Right, in which one was Lord Nelson born?" Anywhere near Marsham prompted the poser: "Who can remember the famous agricultural workers' champion born over there?" A day out in Gressenhall might invite a spot of workhouse history. A Swaffham safari could lead to treasure trove…

It became a long-running challenge to come up with someone or something interesting connected with each place we were visiting or passing through. Easier for me as a full-time passenger, of course, but a good habit to cultivate along a Norfolk trail full of variety and intrigue.

Questions are split into various categories, some of them sorted to suit specific areas of the county where holidaymakers have been known to seek enlightenment. I hope the section on local literature will lure book-lovers to second-hand departments for possible bargains of their own as well as to shelves packed with the latest home-grown delights in the county's rich array of bookshops.

Village inquiries offer a golden chance to support local shops, post offices, churches and pubs – and to go in search of die-hard natives able to throw valuable light on local history and strange dialect.

Yes, quiz compilers do have a show-off streak, glorying in their knowledge and power as they fire away at a captive audience. I've been busy for about 60 years finding material for a volume like this, so a slight air of supremacy must be forgiven. Deep down, I really want to share my love of Norfolk and this could be an ideal way to do it.

I salute all who have lit my Norfolk way since a country childhood blessed with so many generous lantern-carriers. More recent benefactors include Jeremy Nottingham, question-setter for the Sheringham Town Quiz over several years, and my wife Diane who has her own ways of probing to complement my travels and vast collection of books.

Please don't cheat simply because there's no-one on hand to check if you sneak a peep at the answers. Remember, there's no shame in adding to your Norfolk expertise after frankly admitting: "Cor, blarst, I dint know that!"

Keith Skipper
Cromer, 2008

Keith Skipper's

NORFOLK QUIZ BOOK

You can always tell a Norfolk man -
but you can't tell him much!

HALSGROVE

First published in Great Britain in 2008

Copyright © 2008 Keith Skipper

British Library Cataloguing-in-Publication Data
A CIP record for this title is available from the British Library

ISBN 978 1 84114 833 5

HALSGROVE
Halsgrove House, Ryelands Industrial Estate,
Bagley Road, Wellington, Somerset TA21 9PZ
Tel: 01823 653777   Fax: 01823 216796
email: sales@halsgrove.com
website: www.halsgrove.com

Printed and bound by Short Run Press, Exeter

Warm-Up Round

1. What would you do with floaters, sinkers and swimmers?

2. There are only two villages in Norfolk beginning with the letter "Q". Quidenham is one – name the other.

3. Where was the railway station which served the Sandringham royal estate until 1966?

4. What is a native of Sheringham called?

5. Which castle did Sir John Fastolf complete building in 1454?

6. Where can you find the largest area of ancient woodland in Norfolk?

7. Who reintroduced the growing of flax in Norfolk in 1931?

8. Which Norfolk village was home to the Reeve of Chaucer's Canterbury Tales?

9. Which Norfolk writer became an agent for the British Bible Society?

10. What was the name of the original Pedlar of Swaffham, who found great riches after a trip to London?

Around the Villages

1. In which village was fisherman and traditional singer Sam Larner born in 1878?

2. Which inland village can you enter but not pass through?

3. Which place is disguised in the anagram "man ties wall light"?

4. Where was historian Francis Blomefield village rector in the 18th century?

5. Which coastal settlement is known as the Village of Millionaires?

6. Which village name in mid-Norfolk means "gravelly nook"?

7. Which village was visited by poet William Wordsworth in 1790?

8. There are only two Norfolk villages with as few as three letters in their name – Oby, 10 miles north-west of Yarmouth is one. Name the other.

9. Where was the only Gilbertine monastery in Norfolk?

10. Which doctor wrote a village history of Litcham?

11. In which village was the hall rebuilt as the North family seat in 1695?

12. Which village windmill was acquired in 1965 by the Norfolk Windmills Trust as its first for preservation?

13. What began on April 1st, 1914 in a village not far from Diss and went on until the outbreak of the second world war?

14. What was produced for 30 years in a factory at South Creake run by George Money?

15. William Fellowes founded the Norfolk and Norwich Hospital in 1771. Where did he set up what is believed to be the first cottage hospital in the country a few years earlier?

16. John Aylmer was tutor to Lady Jane Gray before he became Bishop of London. In which village was he born?

17. Where was the famous royal surgeon Astley Cooper born in 1768?

18. Which great inventor is buried in the village churchyard at Hilgay, three miles south of Downham Market?

19. Where was Nurse Edith Cavell born in 1865, the daughter of the village rector?

20. Name the two Norfolk villages which begin with the letter Y.

Picture Poser 1

With this manager at the helm, Norwich City Football Club reached the top flight for the first time when they won the Second Division Championship in 1971-72. Name him.

Dialect Delights

1. What would a Norfolk farmworker do with a dockey?

2. Where would you wear a chummy?

3. Who wrote *The Boy John Letters* in dialect to the *Eastern Daily Press* from 1946 to 1958?

4. What would you be if you were shanny?

5. Where could a Norfolk housewife make one pie out of a million?

6. Who wrote two books called *Broad Norfolk* in 1949 and 1973?

7. What would you do with a hutkin?

8. What is the dialect word for close or oppressive weather?

9. Who translated the *Song of Solomon* into the Norfolk dialect in 1862?

10. What in Norfolk dialect is a higgler?

11. What would you be if you were all of a muckwash?

12. What is a pightle in Norfolk?

13. How would you catch a pollywiggle?

14. What would you do with a thrape?

15. What is a King Harry?

16. What would you be if you were winneking?

17. What is the Norfolk dialect word for a scarecrow?

18. What would you do with pinpaunches?

19. Whose *Vocabulary of East Anglia*, was first published in 1838, five years after his death?

20. Where was Allan Smethurst, The Singing Postman, born in 1927?

The Singing Postman

This highly individual church tower, rising above marshland just inside the Norfolk border, constantly intrigues holidaymakers on the River Waveney. Where is it?

Local Literature

1. Which famous playwright rented a farmhouse in Felbrigg, near Cromer, in 1892 to improve his health and work on his latest play?

2. Who wrote *The Story of a Norfolk Farm*, first published in 1941?

3. What was the real name of Breckland writer Michael Home?

4. Whose Norfolk novels were called *Paper Trail* and *Sound Track*?

5. Who wrote the poem *On a Friend's Escape From Drowning off the Norfolk Coast*?

6. Which Norfolk resort became *Anchorstone* in L. P. Hartley's novels?

7. What do the initials R.H. stand for in the name of Norfolk writer R.H. Mottram?

8. Which Victorian novelist sent heroine Margaret Hale to Cromer for a rest cure?

9. Which pupil destined to become a famous poet enlisted at Gresham's School in Holt in September 1920?

10. Whose first novel, *Death Under Sail*, is a thriller set on the Norfolk Broads?

11. Who was the Norfolk poet and dramatist who became Poet Laureate after John Dryden in 1668?

12. Who turned Horsey Mere into *Hurle Mere* in a Victorian novel?

13. Where is author Henry Rider Haggard buried?

14. Which famous writer is buried in Langham churchyard?

15. Which famous writer was born in Great Yarmouth in 1830?

16. Who wrote *Coot Club*, a children's adventure story set on the Norfolk Broads?

17. Whose debut novel in 1995 was *Gorleston*?

18. Whose poem *Norfolk* begins: "How did the Devil come? When first attack?"

19 Who was the prolific author, farmer and long-term campaigner in the "tithe wars" who lived at Wortham Manor?

20. Which best-selling novel by Jack Higgins, published in 1975, is set in north Norfolk?

He was known as The People's Naturalist who lived for 40 years with his family at Wheatfen Broad, Surlingham, in a remote cottage by a reedy wilderness. Name him.

Personality Parade

1. Which Norfolk social reformer was known as the Gay Quaker?

2. Who said of the Norfolk Broads in 1883: "There is no better playground in England and certainly none easier of access or more cheaply to be enjoyed"?

3. Who published the first large-scale maps of Norfolk in 1797?

4. What did Great Yarmouth's District General Hospital (at Gorleston) become in 1984?

5. Who built the first sluice at Denver, near Downham Market, in 1651 as part of a scheme to drain the fens?

6. Which famous writer stayed at the Royal Hotel, Yarmouth's first seaside hotel, which opened in 1848?

7. Who was the first agricultural labourer to enter Parliament when he became a Norfolk MP in 1885?

8. Who is Norfolk's patron saint of agriculture?

9. Who was the Irish showman who turned Norwich Theatre Royal into one of the most successful in Europe after taking over in 1972?

10. Who founded Lotus Cars and then moved the company to Norfolk?

Pews and Preachers

1. Why is the parish church at Bixley, near Norwich, so special?

2. Where was the only church in the county to be destroyed in a wartime aircraft crash in 1944?

3. Which Archbishop of Canterbury was born at West Dereham, four miles south-east of Downham Market?

4. Who was the first Methodist preacher in Norfolk?

5. In which parish church can you find memorials to the Spelman family?

6. In which village were Lord Nelson's grandfather, father and brother all rectors?

7. Which village church clock bears the text "Watch and Pray" instead of numerals?

8. Who was the Fighting Bishop of Norwich?

9. Who wrote *The Spreading Flame*, a book on the coming of Methodism to Norfolk?

10. Who was Rector of Ashill for 76 years from 1813 until 1889 – the longest incumbency on record?

A family mausoleum in the shape of a pyramid, rated the finest in England, suddenly emerges out of the trees. Where will you find it?

Stage and Screen

1. Who wrote the screen play for the Norfolk-shot film of L.P.Hartley's *The Go-Between* in 1971?

2. Whose play *The Kitchen* (1957) was inspired by experiences working at the Bell Hotel in Norwich?

3. Who was the male star of the film *Conflict of Wings* (1953) in which the Broadland village of Hickling played a key role?

4. The 1945 film version of *The Wicked Lady* starred Margaret Lockwood and James Mason. Which famous Norfolk building also had a starring role?

5. Which Norfolk landmark was destroyed by fire in the 1967 film shocker *The Shuttered Room*?

6. Alec Guinness starred in *Barnacle Bill*, one of the last Ealing Comedies made in 1957. In which Norfolk resort was it filmed?

7. St Benet's Abbey and Hickling on the Norfolk Broads featured in the 1951 smuggling tale *Green Grow the Rushes*. Who was the young actor on parade destined for international stardom?

8. What was the name of the world war two drama filmed partly on location at Holkham in 1965 starring George Peppard and Sophia Loren?

9. Which Lincolnshire-born impresario was in charge of the Norwich Theatre Royal for 30 years from 1926?

10. Who founded the Maddermarket Theatre company in Norwich in the 1920s?

This Sporting Life

1. Which Australian Test cricketer saw service at RAF Great Massingham during the second world war?

2. Who scored Norwich City's first goal on their new ground at Carrow Road in 1935?

3. Which Norfolk rider helped Britain win the Three-Day Event at the Mexico Olympics in 1968?

4. When did speedway racing first come to Norfolk?

5. Which Norwich boxer fought for the British Middleweight championship against Jock McAvoy in 1939?

6. Which famous cricketer was born in the village of Horningtoft five miles south-east of Fakenham, in 1804?

7. Who was Norwich City Football Club's first professional manager, appointed in 1905?

8. Where in Norfolk was Jem Mace, father of modern scientific boxing, born in 1831?

9. Who enjoyed a continuous span of 60 years in office in one capacity or another after taking over as captain of Norfolk County Cricket Club in 1912?

10. Who might be found running at The Walks?

He founded Norwich Union, one of the largest insurance organisations in the world, after moving to Norfolk from Kent in 1783. Name him.

The City Beat

1. St Giles' Hospital was founded in Norwich by Bishop Walter Suffield in 1249. What is the building commonly known as today?

2. Which Norwich school did Norfolk, Middlesex and England cricketer Bill Edrich attend?

3. Who became the first mayor in 1403 when Henry IV made Norwich a city?

4. The building of Norwich Cathedral by Herbert de Losinge began in 1096. Where did most of the stone come from?

5. Which architect created the Royal Arcade in Norwich?

6. Which Norwich printer, born in 1752, is remembered each day in the House of Commons?

7. Who founded the international Round Table movement in Norwich in 1927?

8. Who was knighted in Norwich by Charles II in 1671?

9. Which notable Norwich building was erected by textile merchant Robert Toppes around 1450?

10. Who walked in front of Norwich mayoral processions to clear the way, a tradition started early in the 15th century?

North Norfolk

1. Whose memorial is a stone water trough on the outskirts of Cromer?

2. Who created the park around Sheringham Hall in the 19th century and is buried at Aylsham?

3. Who gave Felbrigg Hall, near Cromer, to the National Trust?

4. Which director general of the BBC was educated at Gresham's School in Holt?

5. Norfolk's lone militant Jacobite was executed at Tyburn in 1723. He is remembered with an inscribed tablet on a house in Aylsham. Who was he?

6. John Gresham converted his manor in Holt into a free grammar school in the 1550s. Which Guild was responsible for the school's management?

7. John Fryer was Master of The Bounty, the ship at the heart of the most famous mutiny in maritime history. Where was his Norfolk home?

8. Which were the Glaven Ports?

9. Where in Cromer would you find Harry Yaxley's hole?

10. Who succeeded William Wilberforce as leader of the anti-slavery party and spent his last years at Northrepps Hall?

The Cathedral of the Fields is a magnificent monument to Victorian enthusiasm. Where will you find this many-pinnacled parish church?

Great Yarmouth and District

1. What was Yarmouth given permission to build in 1261?

2. Who was the Norfolk Giant, born in West Somerton, nine miles north west of Yarmouth, in 1820? He is buried in the village churchyard.

3. Nelson's Monument in Yarmouth, standing 144ft high, was built by public subscription in 1819. Who stands on top?

4. Who set up the first holiday camp in England at Caister-on-Sea?

5. Miles Corbet was both Recorder and MP at Yarmouth. What else marks him out in history?

6. James Haylett is responsible for the most telling line in local seafaring history at the opening of the inquest into the tragedy of the Caister lifeboat in 1901. Nine of the crew were lost. Haylett exclaimed: "Caister men never turn back". What was the name of the lifeboat?

7. What happened to the Caister lifeboat in 1969?

8. Under what pen-name did Yarmouth naturalist Arthur Patterson (1857 – 1935) write?

9. What was "Mr Cap" doing around Yarmouth in 1964?

10. What famous Yarmouth landmark on the Golden Mile was demolished for scrap during the second world war?

Diss and District

1. Who was Rector of Diss for 25 years from 1504 until his death and generally considered to be the first Poet Laureate?

2. Which Poet Laureate of the 20th century voted Diss his favourite English town?

3. Where can you find a museum dedicated to the TV comedy series Dad's Army?

4. Which family provided rectors at Diss Parish Church in an unbroken sequence from 1778 to 1916?

5. Where was Mary Tudor staying in 1555 when she wrote to the Privy Council asserting her right to the throne following the death of her brother Edward VI?

6. Gaymer's Cider is associated with Attleborough, but where did it originate?

7. Which wife of a former British Prime Minister lived in Diss as a child?

8. Who did Diss Town's footballers beat at Wembley in 1994 to win the FA Vase?

9. What was held at Cock Street Green in Diss from the mid 15th century until the 1870s?

10. Who was the famous composer and writer of madrigals baptised in Diss in 1574?

Picture Poser 7

Born in King's Lynn, she made a bold mark in the literary world and in Royal circles. Name her.

Round East Dereham Way

1. Who was the rector of Dereham who gained notoriety for burning about 200 people at the stake?

2. The old workhouse at Gressenhall is now a museum of rural life two miles north-west of Dereham. Why was the workhouse nicknamed "The spike"?

3. Which famous hymn writer came to live in Dereham in 1736 and is buried in the churchyard?

4. In which village, five miles north of Dereham, can you find the oldest remains of a Saxon cathedral?

5. Which saint features prominently on the Dereham town sign erected in 1954 at the entrance to the Market Place?

6. In September, 1915, many buildings in Dereham were destroyed and two people lost their lives. What caused the damage?

7. Who was the Victorian vicar of Dereham famous for his diary?

8. Who was the rector of Scarning, two miles west of Dereham, a great scholar, writer and former headmaster of the Norwich School who died in 1914 at the age of 91?

9. Who built the Theatre Royal in Dereham in 1812 as a base for his travelling family theatre company?

10. In St Nicholas churchyard in Dereham is a memorial stone to Jean de Narde who died in the town in 1799. Who was he?

Swaffham and District

1. Swaffham's Market Cross was built in 1783. Which goddess is depicted in the statue on the top?

2. Who founded the castle at Castle Acre soon after the Norman Conquest?

3. Which famous Egyptologist was raised in Swaffham before joining Lord Carnarvon to find a famous tomb?

4. Where can you find a replica of an Iceni village?

5. Which famous author was once a sanitary inspector for Swaffham Rural District Council?

6. Name one of three lay preachers from Swaffham Methodist Church who became members of parliament during the 20th century.

7. Who was the craftsman who made many of the village and town signs in Norfolk? He was a teacher at Hamond's Grammar School in Swaffham.

8. Swaffham featured prominently in the television series *Kingdom*, starring Stephen Fry. What fictitious name was the town given?

9. Which family have lived at Oxburgh Hall since it was built at the end of the Wars of the Roses?

10. Which vicar of Necton, four miles east of Swaffham, wrote a poem in praise of Norfolk in the 1920s? It included the line "It's on the road to nowhere".

Where will you find this ornamental well on a village green?

Thetford and District

1. Political writer Thomas Paine was born in Thetford in 1737. What was his father's main occupation?

2. Which famous naturalist is supposed to have named the area Breckland in the 1890s?

3. Five villages near Thetford were evacuated in 1942 by order of the War Office to be used for training of troops. Name them.

4. According to legend, which wood near Watton is the setting for the story of the Babes in the Wood?

5. Which local estate did Prince Frederick Duleep Singh buy in 1863?

6. In which year did Thetford Borough Council and the London County Council sign the formal agreement regarding overspill population?

7. In which church will you find a memorial to a former rector who was appropriately named Ralf Fuloflove?

8. Who is Betty Ratcliffe and what is her connection with Thetford's Bell Hotel?

9. What is the name of Watton's open air swimming pool?

10. What is the nickname given to the Thetford and Watton railway line, opened in 1869?

West Norfolk

1. Who was imprisoned in the castle at Castle Rising in 1350?

2. When did Hunstanton pier disappear?

3. Who was the King's Lynn woman, born in 1373, who dictated the first known autobiography in the English language

following her pilgrimage over Europe and the Holy Land?

4. How did King John lose his treasure as he crossed The Wash in 1216?

5. Which King's Lynn building, an embodiment of commercial property, went up to replace an earlier one destroyed by fire in 1421?

6. The Native American princess Pocahontas spent nearly a year in Heacham with her husband. Who was he?

7. Which king gave Lynn its freedom so its name could be changed from Bishop's Lynn to King's Lynn?

8. Who bought Sandringham House for a royal residence?

9. Where can bands of brown carrstone and red mid-cretaceous limestone be seen together?

10. Where would you find an old gunpowder store in a village between Docking and Heacham?

Picture Poser 9

This Norwich-born writer became the first woman journalist to join a big London daily newspaper. Name her.

More Town Teasers

1. Which Norfolk town was granted to John of Gaunt by his father Edward III in 1372?

2. Printing was Fakenham's main industry for many years. Who were the town's first recorded printers?

3. Where does a market cross built in 1616 serve as a tourist information centre?

4. What caused the death of about 7000 people in Great Yarmouth in the middle of the 14th century?

5. Which town has the unique distinction of having three parish churches in the same churchyard?

6. Where did the Earl of Orford found the first coursing club in the country in 1786?

7. Which parish church tower has been a ruin since 1724?

8. Where can you find a war memorial in the middle of the town commemorating battles of the Crimea War (1854 – 1856)?

9. What makes Hunstanton unique as a resort?

10. Robert Kett led 20.000 Norfolk rebels in 1549 against social and economic injustices particularly the enclosure of common land. Where did he come from and what was his job?

Myths and Legends

1. Where is it claimed a cobbler set up shop inside a tree?

2. Who is said to have been saved from drowning by a colony of beavers?

3. Where can you find a parish church dedicated to the Head of St John the Baptist?

4. How did locals make the feathers fly at Wreningham, eight miles south of Norwich?

5. Where are you most likely to encounter The Brown Lady?

6. Where will you find the Shrieking Pits?

7. Which village sign features a very handy sword?

8. Where will you find Margaret Read's heart in King's Lynn?

9. Which hall is said to be haunted by at least six members of the Brograve family?

10. Who was the female Scarlet Pimpernel from Ketteringham, six miles south-west of Norwich?

Norfolk had a Dome long before London got in on the act. Where is the local version?

Spot the Location

1. Thaw your ice-cream on the policeman

2. A hard one to turn

3. Prickly pork

4. Taking the tails off

5. Whistle on the rock

6. Arctic agents

7. Sour circle

8. Half a policeman's weapon

9. The value of Attila

10. Visitor's candle

11. Garden implement

12. Carried on snoozing

13. How you come to be born

14. Fred Flintstone's neighbour

15. Tiny waterhole

16. Forest bike

17. Seen in fields at harvest time

18. Heavy insects

19. Like a chin before shaving

20. Cereal and sugar

This Victorian father-figure began a tradition that big profits can come from what is left on the plate! Name him and his product.

Anagram Fun

1. Mow my hand

2. Nat shot nun

3. The hog pie tram

4. Push big harp

5. She rang him

6. Dam the workman

7. Nutters won

8. Nay be elk

9. Slam hay

10. Lot can wrench

11. Link leg

12. Three lettings

13. Male task

14. Open hot crabs

15. Hating mitre

16. Storming

17. Pen trough

18. Pam here

19. Ann's woven sort

20. Send muley

Picture Poser 12

An aerial view of one of North Norfolk's most outstanding properties. Identify it.

Tough Final Test

1. Where will you find the village of Merrivale?

2. Which Norfolk country house has a collection of 20,000 toy soldiers?

3. What were Norwich City Football Club's colours before they adopted yellow and green?

4. Where does the 57-mile Weavers Way begin and end?

5. How many Norfolk lighthouses are there?

6. Who was the King's Lynn explorer who left local names along the north-west Canada coast?

7. Where does the watercolour artist Arthur C Carrick reside when in Norfolk?

8. Who danced The Lancers by himself?

9. What other office does the Abbot of St Benet's hold?

10. Sarah Hare is said to have died after pricking her finger. What is her strange memorial?

PICTURE POSERS ANSWERS

Picture Poser 1 Ron Saunders, who went on to manage other clubs including Manchester City and Aston Villa.

Picture Poser 2 St Mary's Church at Burgh St Peter can be found about two miles east of the village. The tower serves as a memorial or mausoleum to Samuel Boycott who built it in 1793 and lies buried beneath it. The Boycotts were rectors here from 1764 until 1899.

Picture Poser 3 Ted Ellis (1909 – 1986), naturalist, broadcaster and writer, was also Keeper of Natural History at Norwich Castle Museum from 1928 until 1956. Wheatfen Broad, about five miles east of Norwich, is now a nature reserve run by the Ted Ellis Trust.

Picture Poser 4 This fine pyramid is in the extensive park surrounding Blickling Hall, near Aylsham. It contains the remains of John Hobart who became 2nd Earl of Buckingham in 1756, and his family.

Picture Poser 5 Thomas Bignold (1761 – 1835), who is buried in the churchyard at Old Catton, just outside Norwich. The family name dominated Norwich Union until Sir Robert Bignold retired in 1964.

Picture Poser 6 St Michael's and all Angels Parish Church at Booton, near Reepham, was created by Whitwell Elwin, rector here for 50 years. He began rebuilding in the 1870s and included details from as far afield as Venice and Egypt.

Picture Poser 7 Fanny Burney (1752 – 1840) enjoyed great success with her first novel *Evelina* and mingled with big names of the day including Sir Joshua Reynolds and Dr Johnson. On being introduced to society she took the post of Keeper of the Robes to Queen Charlotte.

Picture Poser 8 This structure of red brick with terracotta dressings was erected on Heydon village green by Col. W. E. G. Lytton-Bulwer in 1887 to mark Queen Victoria's Golden Jubilee. Picturesque Heydon is four miles west of Aylsham.

Picture Poser 9 Harriet Martineau (1802 – 1876), born without the senses of taste and smell and deaf by the time she was 18, overcame these and many other obstacles to become leader writer on the Daily News in 1852.

Picture Poser 10 Norfolk's Dome is on the old airfield at Langham, seven miles south-east of Wells-next-the-Sea, and was built as an anti-aircraft training device in the second world war. Film was projected onto the inside of the dome and trainee gunners practiced dry-firing at images on the film.

Picture Poser 11 Jeremiah Colman (1830 – 1898), mustard magnate and benevolent employer who moved his business to Carrow in Norwich so goods could be shipped down the river. He built the first mustard mill – and Colman's has been the best-known name in the mustard business ever since.

Picture Poser 12 Sheringham Hall, a Grade II listed property dating back to 1813, is attached to the National Trust's Sheringham Park. It has 10 bedrooms and 20,000 sq ft of living space.

WARM-UP ROUND ANSWERS

1. Eat them – they are types of Norfolk dumplings.
2. Quarles, a tiny community four miles south-west of Wells-next-the-Sea.
3. Wolferton – not to be confused with Wolterton, near Aylsham.
4. A Shannock. Some claim that a true Shannock is someone whose parents and grand-parents were born in the town.
5. Caister, near Great Yarmouth, now home to a collection of vintage cars.
6. Foxley Wood, seven miles north-east of East Dereham, covering about 300 acres and basically unaltered since the Domesday Book. It is cared for by the Norfolk Naturalist Trust.
7. King George V at West Newton on the Sandringham Estate.
8. Bawdeswell, seven miles north-east of East Dereham.
9. George Borrow (1803–1881), author of the books *Lavengro* and *Romany Rye*.
10. John Chapman who features on the town sign and in the parish church where there is a carving of him and his dog at the end of a pew.

AROUND THE VILLAGES ANSWERS

1. Winterton, eight miles north-east of Yarmouth. Sam was "discovered" when he was nearly 80. He died at 87 after a few brief years of fame.
2. Heydon, six miles west of Aylsham. This attractive estate village gathered about a green is at the end of a cul-de-sac that leads to Heydon Hall.
3. Little Walsingham, known as England's Nazareth. It draws thousands of pilgrims each year to the Shrine of Our Lady.
4. Fersfield, near Diss, from 1729 until his death in 1752. He printed his *History of Norfolk* on his own press at the rectory.
5. Overstrand, a couple of miles south-east of Cromer. Six millionaires had homes there at the turn of the 20th century, including Lord Battersea.
6. Gressenhall, three miles north-west of East Dereham, from the Old English greosn (gravel) and halh (nook, corner of land).
7. Forncett St Peter, eight miles north of Diss, to see his sister, Dorothy at the rectory. She was staying with her uncle the Rev William Cookson and his wife.
8. Hoe, two miles north of East Dereham.
9. Shouldham, nine miles south-east of King's Lynn. It was the last double monastery of canons and nuns established, all subsequent Gilbertine houses were for canons alone.
10. Dr Eric Puddy. The book was first published in 1957.
11. Rougham, eight miles north of Swaffham.
12. Billingford, two miles east of Diss. There's another Billingford six miles north of East Dereham.

13. Burston School Strike, longest in English history. It was started by pupils after teachers Tom and Kitty Higdon were sacked.
14. Razor blades, from the 1920s.
15. Shotesham, six miles south of Norwich.
16. Tilney St Lawrence, seven miles south-west of King's Lynn, in 1521.
17. Brooke, seven miles south of Norwich, where his father was curate. He was surgeon to George IV. A street in the village bears the surgeon's name – Astley Cooper Place.
18. George Manby (1765 – 1854), whose inventions included rocket lifesaving apparatus, a chemical fire extinguisher, elastic sheets for use at fires, harpoons for whaling and improved types of lifeboats, howitzers and dredgers.
19. Swardeston, four miles south-west of Norwich. She was shot by the Germans for helping Allied soldiers escape during the first world war and is buried at a spot called Life's Green outside Norwich Cathedral.
20. Yaxham, two miles south of East Dereham and Yelverton, five miles south-east of Norwich.

DIALECT DELIGHTS ANSWERS

1. Eat it – it's his dinner taken to the field in a dockey bag.
2. On your head – it's a soft felt hat.
3. Comedian Sidney Grapes of Potter Heigham.
4. Excited, wild, scatter-brained.
5. In the kitchen – a million is the Norfolk name for a pumpkin.
6. Eric Fowler, who wrote under the pseudonym of Jonathan Mardle for the *Eastern Daily Press*.
7. Use it – it's a sheath for a sore finger.
8. Thongy.
9. The Rev Edward Gillett, Vicar of Runham, near Yarmouth. It was printed with translations for 23 other counties at the expense of Prince Louis Bonaparte.
10. A dealer. To higgle is to bargain or argue – like haggle.
11. Hot and bothered.
12. A small field or enclosure.
13. In a jar – it's a tadpole.
14. Eat it – it's a gooseberry.
15. A bird – the goldfinch.
16. Whinging.
17. A mawkin, it is featured in the logo for the Friends Of Norfolk Dialect (FOND).
18. Eat them – they are winkles.
19. The Rev Robert Forby, Rector of Fincham, five miles north-east of Downham Market from 1801 until his death in 1825.
20. Bury, in Lancashire.

LOCAL LITERATURE ANSWERS

1. Oscar Wilde. The play, *A Woman of No Importance*, emerged the following year.

2. Henry Williamson, author of *Tarka the Otter*, who left Devon for a run-down farm at Stiffkey in North Norfolk.

3. Christopher Bush, born in 1885 wrote military adventures and over 50 detective novels under his real name. His Norfolk books, including *Autumn Fields*, *Spring Sowing* and *Winter Harvest*, underlined his deep affection for Breckland.

4. John Timpson, who retired to Norfolk after a distinguished broadcasting career with the BBC. He worked for the local press at East Dereham in the 1950s.

5. George Barker (1913 – 1991) who lived for several years at Itteringham. He is buried in the local churchyard.

6. Hunstanton, in the *Eustace and Hilda* trilogy. Hartley (1895 – 1972) played beneath the sandstone cliffs as a child.

7. Ralph Hales Mottram (1883 – 1971), who made his big literary mark with *The Spanish Farm Trilogy* in 1927.

8. Elizabeth Gaskell in *North and South*, first published in 1855.

9. W.H. Auden. The school now has a theatre named after him.

10. C.P. Snow (1905 – 1980) was still working as molecular physicist when he wrote *Death Under Sail* in 1932.

11. Thomas Shadwell, Restoration wit and playwright, was born at Stanton Hall, near Weeting.

12. Wilkie Collins in *Armadale*, first published in 1866.

13. On his death in 1925 at the age of 68, Sir Henry's ashes were buried in the family vault in the chancel of St Mary's Church at Ditchingham. There's also a window there in his memory.

14. Frederick Marryat (1792 -1848), who retired to the village, seven miles south-east of Wells-next-the-Sea, after a distinguished naval career. Seven novels belong to the Langham period, including *Children of the New Forest*.

15. Anna Sewell, who wrote *Black Beauty*, one of the world's best-selling books with over 30 million copies sold. The house where she was born nestles in the north-east corner of Yarmouth Market Place in the shadow of the parish church.

Frederick Marryat

16. Arthur Ransome (1884 – 1967), a regular visitor to the area.

17. Henry Sutton, who was born in the village of Hopton just south of the town in 1963. His novel *Bank Holiday Monday* is set around Burnham Overy Staithe.

18. John Betjeman, who wrote it in 1958. He had strong links with Norfolk and was a regular visitor, especially to look round churches.

19. Doreen Wallace (1897 – 1989). Her real name was Doreen Rash, but she wrote over 50 books under the pen-name of Doreen Wallace. On her death at 92, the Eastern Daily Press called her "a latter-day Boadicea".

20. *The Eagle Has Landed*. It was also made into a successful film in 1977, starring Michael Caine.

PERSONALITY PARADE ANSWERS

1. Novelist and poet Amelia Opie (1769 – 1853). Opie Street, between Castle Meadow and London Street in Norwich, was laid out on the site of the last house she lived in. There is also a statue of her on that street.

2. George Christopher Davies, known as the Man who Discovered the Broads.

3. William Faden, (1750 -1836) geographer to King George III and the Prince of Wales. He published many maps during his career. A catalogue of his works in 1822 included 350 items.

4. It was renamed the James Paget Hospital after the leading surgeon of his day. Paget was born in Great Yarmouth in 1814 and died in 1899. His family had been in the town for 200 years.

James Paget

5. Dutch engineer Cornelius Vermuyden (1590 – 1677) was knighted by Charles I in 1629 before his major work on drainage of the Fens.

6. Charles Dickens.

7. Warwickshire-born Joseph Arch. He won North West Norfolk for the Liberals.

8. Saint Walstan (961 – 1016) He was born at Bawburgh, five miles west of Norwich, where the waters of his well became renowned for curative properties. The parish church is still a centre for pilgrimage and each year a procession is made to the famous well with a service of blessing performed.

9. Dick Condon, who died aged 54 in 1991. He resigned as general manager after a clash with the theatre trust over a proposed £2.75m refurbishment scheme.

10. Colin Chapman, who died aged 54 in 1982. He moved Lotus Cars from London to the former airfield at Hethel, seven miles south-west of Norwich, in 1966.

PEWS AND PREACHERS ANSWERS

1. It's the only one in England dedicated in honour of St Wandregesilius. This is the Latinised form of St Wandrille, a 7th century French abbot.

2. All Saints' Church at Bawdeswell. A Mosquito bomber based at Downham Market was returning from a bombing raid over Germany in November, 1944 when it crashed on the church, which had been rebuilt in 1845. A new church was completed 10 years after the wartime crash. It is in classic Colonial style.

All Saints' Church at Bawdeswell, victim of a wartime crash.

3. Hubert Walter, who took up the post under Richard I in 1193. He was also Lord Chief Justice of England, Lord High Chancellor and Governor of the Realm. He founded a monastery on returning to West Dereham and it is still possible to trace remains at the Abbey Farm.

4. James Wheatley, a Welshman. He came to Norwich in 1751.

5. The 15th century church at Narborough, eight miles south-east of King's Lynn.

6. Hilborough, five miles south of Swaffham. During the 18th century the patronage of All Saints' Church belonged to the Nelson family and from 1734 until 1806 every rector was a Nelson – except for one who married a Nelson.

7. All Saints at Westacre, five miles north-west of Swaffham.

8. Bishop Henry Despenser,(1341 – 1406) who put down the Peasant's Revolt in Norfolk with awful cruelty in 1381.

9. Cyril Jolly, of Gressenhall, three miles north-west of East Dereham. He was a local preacher and prolific writer. His books included the definitive biography of Cromer lifeboat coxswain Henry Blogg.

10. The Rev Bartholomew Edwards. He died just nine days short of his 100th birthday. He never retired, never went away for a holiday and hardly missed a service. The east window in his parish church was replaced by the present stained glass one in 1900 in his memory.

STAGE AND SCREEN
ANSWERS

1. Harold Pinter.
2. Arnold Wesker.
3. John Gregson.
4. Blickling Hall.
5. Hardingham Mill.
6. Hunstanton.
7. Richard Burton.
8. Operation Crossbow.
9. Jack Gladwin.
10. Nugent Monck.

Nugent Monck

THIS SPORTING LIFE ANSWERS

1. All-rounder Keith Miller, who flew Mosquitoes with 169 Squadron.
2. Team captain Doug Lochhead in a 4:3 win over West Ham.
3. Major Derek Alhusen of Claxton Manor, seven miles south-east of Norwich
4. 1932, at The Firs Stadium in Norwich.
5. Arthur "Ginger" Sadd, who lost narrowly on points over 15 rounds.
6. Fuller Pilch, England's top batsman for a decade. He was lured away from Norfolk to play for Kent after being offered £100 a year.
7. John Bowman. He was appointed when City turned professional and joined the Southern League. He resigned in 1907.
8. Beeston, near East Dereham. There is a memorial in the village churchyard.
9. Michael Falcon. He played for Norfolk for 40 years, 34 of them as captain. He served on the committee, was chairman for 19 years and president for the last three of his "reign".
10. King's Lynn footballers – it's the name of their ground.

THE CITY BEAT ANSWERS

1. The Great Hospital. This is one of the oldest foundations in the city and was a home for 30 distressed clergy and as a place where 13 old folk and seven poor scholars could have a hot dinner and warm themselves. It just escaped dissolution at the Reformation and was taken over by Norwich Corporation. It is now independently run by trustees.

2. Bracondale School. Founded in 1821, it was closed in 1993. It was a private fee-paying school, for up to 100 boys. The site is now occupied by a housing development.

3. William Appleyard who died in 1419 used to live at what is now the Bridewell Museum having inherited the property in 1386. One of the wealthiest merchants in the city he was a man of considerable political power. He served as mayor for three consecutive terms.

George Skipper

4. Caen, in Normandy. As there is no building stone in Norfolk apart from flint, stone cut to size was brought from Caen by water, brought by boat across the Channel and into the North Sea, by river from the coast and into an excavated canal from the Wensum to a special quay near the Cathedral.

5. George Skipper (1856 – 1948), Norwich's most famous Victorian and Edwardian architect. Built in 1899 the arcade is a magnificent example of Art Nouveau. Born in East Dereham he trained in London before returning to Norwich and setting up his own practice in 1879.

6. Luke Hansard. He became a printer, moved to London and became responsible for printing the House of Commons Journal, an unofficial account of the proceedings. His son, Thomas, bought the Journal and the business remained in the family until

1889 when it was taken over by the Stationary Office. The name Hansard was officially adopted for their reports in 1943.

7. Louis Marchesi (1898 – 1968), a "pastry cook". A Rotarian, he proposed a club "for young men only". In 1937 he was invited to become a national honorary member of Round Table for life. He had a public house named after him in the city.

8. Writer and scholar Sir Thomas Browne, whose statue on Hay Hill was unveiled in 1904. He was a great lover of language and was the first to notice Norfolk had a dialect of its own.

9. Dragon Hall in King Street, the only medieval merchant's trading hall known to survive in Western Europe. It had many uses over the centuries – worker's cottages, rectory, butcher's shop, training centre and pub – before being taken over by the City Council in 1979. Having saved the roof, the council handed the building to the Norfolk and Norwich Heritage Trust which has undertaken all subsequent restoration.

10. A Whiffler. By the early 18th century they wore a distinctive costume of scarlet satin breeches, white satin jerkins and a hat decorated with a cockade of feathers and ribbons. They brandished swords and tossed them in the air. The office was abolished around 1832.

NORTH NORFOLK ANSWERS

1. Clement Scott (1841 – 1904), the writer who "discovered" Poppyland. His articles in the *Daily Telegraph*, coupled with the opening of the railway to the district, helped make it highly fashionable. The water trough memorial, now filled with flowers, was placed on the Overstrand/Northrepps road junction five years after his death.

Clement Scott memorial

2. Humphrey Repton (1752 – 1818). As a watercolour artist he developed the technique of writing and illustrating a "Red Book" for each estate. Sheringham Hall is the best surviving example of Repton's work and was his favourite.

3. R.W. Ketton-Cremer (1906 -1969). He wrote several books with local themes. *Norfolk In the Civil War*, his celebrated portrait of a society in conflict, was first published in the year of his death.

4. Lord John Reith. He became the first Director General of the BBC when it received its Charter in 1927. His fiercely moral stance made him one of the outstanding characters of the age and made the BBC a model for the rest of the world.

5. Christopher Layer (1683 – 1723) He is remembered with the following inscription on a house in Aylsham: "Christopher Layer of Booton lived here. He was a faithful adherent of the House of Stuart and for his loyalty to that cause suffered an ignominious death at Tyburn, 17th May, 1723."

6. The Fishmongers Company. Close links with them continue to this day.

7. Wells-next-the-Sea. Fryer died in 1817 and is buried in the parish churchyard.

8. Blakeney, Cley and Salthouse.

9. Cromer Parish Church tower – it used to give access to the ledge upon which a beacon was lit to help passing ships. Harry Yaxley and a companion were birdnesting from the ledge when Harry fell 20 metres to the ground. He survived the fall to live an active life before he retired and died in Cromer.

10. Thomas Fowell Buxton (1788 – 1845) There is a full-length statue of him in Westminster Abbey where he stands next to his old friend, Wilberforce. He is buried in Overstrand.

GREAT YARMOUTH AND DISTRICT
ANSWERS

1. A town wall. Henry III granted permission to build a wall enclosing an area of 133 acres on three sides, the fourth being protected by the river. Building started in1285.

2. Robert Hales. He grew to 7ft 6in tall and in his prime measured 64 in round the chest and 64 in round the waist and weighed 33 stone.

3. Britannia. She faces inland, looking towards Burnham Thorpe, where Nelson was born in 1758.

4. John Fletcher Dodd. The camp was set up in 1906 as a coastal retreat for London Socialists with campers in tents by the shore. Fame of the camp grew and nearly a thousand people a week came to stay in the summer. Original rules included no alcohol, no bad language, proper one-piece bathing suits, no talking after 11pm and strict sexual segregation.

John Fletcher Dodd

5. He was the only Norfolk man to sign the death warrant of Charles I. After fleeing the country and settling in Holland, he was kidnapped and brought back to England to stand trial. He went to the gallows at Tyburn in 1662 as a regicide affirming yet again that the execution of Charles I was "a necessary and public act of justice."

6. Beauchamp. There is a marble memorial to the victims in a corner of the village cemetery. A Caister public house is called The Never Turn Back.

7. It was axed by the R.N.L.I. and has been independent ever since.

8. John Knowlittle. Breydon Water, the estuary at Great Yarmouth, inspired much of his writing. He wrote 26 books along with hundreds of articles for newspapers, periodicals, leaflets and reports for natural history organisations. Yarmouth honoured him in1957 when they unveiled a tablet in George Street close to where he was born.

9. It was the first drilling rig to start operations of the Norfolk coast in the search for oil and gas.

10. The Revolving Tower which was 125ft tall and built in 1897.

DISS AND DISTRICT ANSWERS

1. John Skelton (1460 – 1529). A former tutor to Prince Henry – later Henry VIII – he is buried in Westminster Abbey.

2. John Betjeman (1906 – 1984) He made short films marking his visits to the town.

3. Bressingham Steam Museum and Gardens, three miles north-west of Diss (there is another one in Thetford).

4. The Manning family. There is a portrait in the church of William Manning who finished 46 years of service in 1857. A brass tablet shows the head of Charles Manning.

5. Kenninghall, seven miles north-west of Diss

6. Banham, six miles north-west of Diss. The Gaymer family had been making cider in the village for several generations before William Gaymer (1805 – 1884) developed the business and founded a company. Poor transport facilities led to the factory being moved to Attleborough in 1896.

John Skelton

7. Mary Wilson, wife of Harold Wilson. She featured in a poem about the town by John Betjeman called *A Minds Journey to Diss.*

8. They beat Taunton 2–1 after extra time.

9. Diss Fair. Too much rowdiness forced its closure by the government in 1872. The original fair was granted a Royal Charter in 1185.

10. John Wilbye. He is probably the most famous of the English madrigalists, and his compositions are often included in modern collections. His most noted is *Weep, weep o mine eyes*. He died in September, 1638.

ROUND EAST DEREHAM WAY
ANSWERS

1. Edmund Bonner, who was Rector in East Dereham from 1534 to 1540. He later became Bishop of London at the time of the heresy trials during Mary Tudor's reign. Bishop Bonner's Cottages stand close to the parish church and are now the town's museum.

2. Male inmates picked oakum from ship's ropes using a spike.

3. William Cowper. There is a window in St Nicholas Parish Church dedicated to his memory.

4. North Elmham. It was the seat of one of the two bishoprics of East Anglia until 1075.

5. St Withburga. Her well can be found outside the west end of the parish church.

6. Bombs dropped from a German Zeppelin

7. The Rev Benjamin Armstrong, vicar from 1850 to 1888.

8. Dr Augustus Jessopp who wrote a number of historical works centred on East Anglia. Material for a memorable collection of essays called *Arcady For Better or Worse* was gleaned from his parishioners, many of them struck by harsh poverty.

Rev Benjamin Armstrong

9. David Fisher (1760 – 1832). In the heydays of the company there were enough Fishers to take up to nine or ten parts in one evening's entertainment.

10. In the Napoleonic Wars the Bell Tower was used as a lodging for French prisoners in transit. Jean de Narde was a young officer who escaped. He was shot and killed and buried in the churchyard.

SWAFFHAM AND DISTRICT ANSWERS

1. Ceres, goddess of the harvest.

Swaffham Market Cross: Ceres, goddess of the harvest

2. William de Warrenne, 1st Earl of Surrey. He fought at Hastings and by the time of the Domesday survey he was one of the wealthiest landowners in England with holdings in 12 counties.

3. Howard Carter, who found the tomb of Tutankhamun in 1923.
4. Cockley Cley, four miles south-west of Swaffham.
5. Capt. W.E. Johns, author of the Biggles adventure stories. He was stationed at Narborough during the first world war.
6. William Taylor, Sidney Dye and Albert (later Lord) Hilton.
7. Harry Carter (1907 – 1983) His first sign was the famous one standing at the entrance to Swaffham Market depicting the story of the Pedlar who found great treasure. The sign was made in 1929. He was a cousin to Howard Carter (see question3).
8. Market Shipborough.
9. The Bedingfields. The hall is seven miles south of Swaffham. Note that the Hall is spelt 'Oxburgh' but the village is 'Oxborough'.
10. Frederick Oakley.

THETFORD AND DISTRICT ANSWERS

1. He made women's corsets
2. W.G.Clarke (1887 – 1925). He gave the region its name in an article in the *Naturalists' Journal* of 1894.
3. Tottington, Lynford, West Tofts, Stamford and Buckenham Toft.
4. Wayland Wood or Wailing Wood as it was once known. The Babes in the Wood is an old English ballad first published in Norwich by Thomas Millington in 1595. No other wood claims any link with this tale and certain facts would indicate that it may even be true.
5. The Elveden Estate, where he enlarged the hall into an oriental extravaganza. A statue of the Prince, who was a great benefactor to Thetford, has been erected in the town.
6. 1957. The first tenants moved in just under two years later.
7. All Saint's, West Harling, seven miles north-east of Thetford.

W.G.Clarke

8. She is supposed to haunt Room 10. She was a landlady there and was murdered by her lover in that room.
9. Loch Neaton.
10. The Crab and Winkle.

WEST NORFOLK ANSWERS

1. Queen Isabella, the She-Wolf of France. She was imprisoned in 1330 by her son, Edward III, for her part in the murder of her husband, Edward II. She died in August, 1358 and her body was buried in London at the Franciscan church in Newgate.
2. It was destroyed by a heavy storm on the night of January 11th, 1978.
3. Margery Kemp (1373 – 1440) the Weeping Wanderer. She wept and sobbed so much throughout her wanderings that other pilgrims avoided her.
4. The tide came in. The baggage train carrying the treasure was trapped on what was then low-lying ground and was lost.
5. Trinity Guildhall which is combined with the town hall. It has a steep roof, large window and chequered patterned exterior and contains some civic treasures in the Regalia Room in the undercroft. The Guildhall itself is not generally open to the public.
6. John Rolfe who was baptised in Heacham in May, 1585. He married Pocahontas in 1614 and they had a son, Thomas. In 1616 they travelled to England and visited Heacham. Pocahontas died in March, 1617 on the eve of their return to Virginia.

7. Henry VIII.
8. Queen Victoria and Prince Albert were looking for a country residence for their son Edward, Prince of Wales. However, the Prince Consort died and Prince Edward visited Sandringham in February, 1862, liked the house and it was bought by Queen Victoria for him for £220,000.
9. Hunstanton Cliffs.

Hunstanton

10. Magazine Cottage in Sedgeford was built by the L'Estrange family during the Civil War. The Hunstanton family tried to offer resistance on the King's behalf against the overwhelming power of the Parliamentary supporters in Norfolk. The house is now a Grade II listed private dwelling and a landmark for walkers on the Peddars Way.

MORE TOWN TEASERS ANSWERS

1. Aylsham, 10 miles north of Norwich, which became the principal town of the Duchy of Lancaster although it's doubtful if John of Gaunt ever visited the area. However, he is remembered in the names of local schools and depicted on the town sign.

2. Stewardsons. They were printing stagecoach posters at the turn of the 19th century and continued printing until 1960.

3. Wymondham. The cross was built in 1617 at a cost of £25. However repairs in 1989 cost £95,000!

4. The Black Death, which reduced the population of the town by two-thirds. It delayed the completion of the town wall and caused work on the western extension of the parish church to be abandoned. It is a possibility that the close proximity of the houses in the famous Yarmouth Rows contributed to the rapid spread of infection.

5. Reepham. All Saints is a ruin. The other two are still open are St Mary's and St Michael's.

6. Swaffham.

7. St Nicholas at North Walsham. This church had the second-tallest steeple in Norfolk until its collapse on May 16th 1724. A further fall in February 1836 during a wintry storm brought down more of the steeple, requiring 50ft to be taken off the remaining east wall as a safety precaution.

8. Attleborough. It stands at the junction of Station Road and Connaught Road and its four sides bear the names of famous battles associated with the war – Balaclava, Inkerman, Alma and Sebastopol. It is rare to find a monument dedicated to this war in any town.

9. It's the only one on the east coast facing west. It takes newcomers and visitors some time to get used to the apparent phenomenon of seeing the sun set over the sea instead of over land.

10. He was a tanner from Wymondham. Kett was defeated at the battle of Dussindale on the outskirts of Norwich, tried for treason, found guilty and hanged at Norwich Castle. In 1949, four centuries after the rebellion, a commemorative plaque was placed at the castle entrance. It reads: "In reparation and honour to a noble and courageous leader in the struggles of the common people of England to escape from a servile life to the freedom of present conditions."

MYTHS AND LEGENDS ANSWERS

1. The Bale Oak was reputed to be 500 years old when it was cut down and carted off in 1860. At between two and three feet from the base it measured 36 feet in circumference. It may have been the remains of a Celtic or Saxon grove in which Christians later built their church of All Saints. The giant tree just outside the church gates could hold up to a dozen men when hollowed out and a cobbler set up his shop and lodge inside it. The little community of Bale nestles off the busy Holt-Fakenham road.

2. St Felix, Bishop of East Anglia for 17 years in the 7th century. His building at Babbingley on the Sandringham Royal Estate six miles north-east of King's Lynn, is now an ivy-clad ruin and was said to be the first Christian church in the region. The village sign depicts a beaver in a bishop's mitre, grasping a bishop's crook. St Felix sailed up the Babbingley river after crossing from Burgundy. His boat got into difficulties and he was saved from drowning, or so legend has it, by a colony of beavers. In gratitude he made the lead beaver a bishop.

3. Trimingham, five miles south-east of Cromer, was said to be the destination of the Head of John the Baptist brought from the fortress of Machaerus, beyond Judea, where the great preacher met his fate. Pilgrims once made their way to this small settlement clinging to the North Norfolk coast. The village hall is still called The Pilgrim Shelter.

4. The legend goes that a 13th century lady of the manor at Wreningham was an evil witch. A knight failed to kill her because she changed into a wren. She is supposed to return every St Stephen's Day and is hunted by villagers who "beat the hedges with sticks and carry the dead wren in triumph!" There have been no reports of such antics in recent years – although the village pub is called the Bird in Hand.

5. Raynham Hall, three miles south-west of Fakenham, is said to be haunted by the Brown Lady on the staircase and passages. It is thought to be the ghost of Dorothy Walpole, wife of the second Viscount Townshend, whom she married in 1713. He gave the care of his six children to his mother at Raynham and perhaps, following her early death from smallpox in 1726, Dorothy returns to seek them.

6. Near Aylmerton, three miles south-east of Cromer, below the so-called Roman Camp, are a number of shallow and circular depressions. These are the Shrieking Pits said to be haunted by a woman in white. Peering into each but failing to find what she seeks, she gives a long shriek and glides on. Some say she is looking for the body of her child buried in one of the pits by her husband who killed both her and the baby in a fit of jealousy.

7. The sign at Winfarthing, four miles north of Diss, offers a reminder that in mediaeval times pilgrims came to seek the help of the Good Sword. It was good for finding things, especially horses – and for losing things. A wife, tired of her husband, only had to set a candle before it every Sunday for a year. That did the trick.

8. Above a window on the north side of the Tuesday Market Place about 12ft from the ground. A small diamond cut into the brickwork encloses a heart. It reputedly marks the spot where the heart of Margaret Read, burnt as a witch in the market place in 1590, landed when it burst from her body.

9. Waxham Hall, now a private residence, four miles east of Stalham. Six Brograves were killed in battle. A late 18th century Brograve invited them all to dinner and drank with them until midnight.... when they vanished.

10. Actress Charlotte Atkyns. During the French Revolution she made several attempts to rescue Queen Marie Antoinette from prison, once even disguising herself as a soldier of the National Guard. There's a memorial to Charlotte on the north wall of the nave of Ketteringham Church.

SPOT THE LOCATION ANSWERS

1. Melton Constable, six miles south-west of Holt.
2. Stiffkey, four miles east of Wells.
3. Thornham, five miles north-east of Hunstanton.
4. Docking, 13 miles south-west of Wells.
5. Kettlestone, three miles north-east of Fakenham.
6. Northrepps, three miles south-east of Cromer.
7. Bittering, five miles north-west of East Dereham.
8. Trunch, three miles north of North Walsham.
9. Hunworth, three miles south of Holt.
10. Guestwick, four miles north-west of Reepham.
11. Hoe, two miles north of East Dereham.
12. Knapton, eight miles south-east of Cromer.
13. Weybourne, seven miles west of Cromer.
14. Barney, six miles north-east of Fakenham.
15. Titchwell, six miles north-east of Hunstanton.
16. Wood Norton, eight miles south-west of Holt.
17. Bale, eight miles north-east of Fakenham.
18. Beeston, seven miles west of East Dereham.
19. Brisley, six miles north-west of East Dereham.
20. Brancaster, seven miles east of Hunstanton.

ANAGRAM FUN ANSWERS

1. Wymondham, 10 miles south-west of Norwich.
2. Hunstanton, 17 miles north-east of King's Lynn.
3. Potter Heigham, 15 miles north-east of Norwich.
4. Happisburgh, seven miles east of North Walsham.
5. Sheringham, four miles west of Cromer.
6. Downham Market, 11 south of King's Lynn.

7. West Runton, two miles west of Cromer.
8. Blakeney, eight miles east of Wells.
9. Aylsham, 12 miles north of Norwich.
10. Clenchwarton, two miles west of King's Lynn.
11. Kelling, three miles north of Holt.
12. Letheringsett, one mile west of Holt.
13. Matlaske, six miles south-east of Holt.
14. Baconsthorpe, seven miles south-west of Cromer.
15. Itteringham, four miles north-west of Aylsham.
16. Grimston, seven miles east of King's Lynn.
17. Gunthorpe, nine miles north-east of Fakenham.
18. Reepham, 12 miles north-west of Norwich.
19. Swanton Novers, six miles south-west of Holt.
20. Mundesley, eight miles south-east of Cromer.

TOUGH FINAL TEST ANSWERS

1. On Great Yarmouth seafront – it's a model village.
2. Houghton Hall. The collection was made by the 6th Marquess of Cholmondeley and moved to the Hall at the opening of the museum. The largest tableau is a reconstruction of the Battle of Waterloo.
3. Blue and white halves. City changed to yellow and green for the 1907-08 season.
4. It is from Cromer to Great Yarmouth.
5. Four – Happisburgh, Gorleston, Hunstanton and Cromer.
6. George Vancouver, 1757 – 1798. His statue stands outside the Custom House in King's Lynn.
7. Sandringham – it's how Prince Charles signs his paintings.
8. Entertainer Richard Hearne as Mr Pastry. He was born in Lady Lane, Norwich, now called Esperanto Way, in 1908. He died in 1979. There is a blue plaque to his memory at the Theatre Royal in Norwich, where he made his debut on stage at six weeks old.
9. The Bishop of Norwich.
10. A wax effigy in the church at Stow Bardolph, two miles north of Downham Market.